WHEREVER

for SATB chorus & piano

NOVELLO

Commissioned by Gareth Malone for Series Four of BBC TV's 'The Choir' and first performed by Malone and The Military Wives Choir as part of The Royal British Legion's Festival of Remembrance at the Royal Albert Hall on 12 November 2011 in the presence of Her Majesty The Queen.

The text is taken from poems, letters and prayers written by the military wives, selected and adapted by Paul Mealor, and a passage from the Book of John:

Wherever you are, my love will keep you safe;
My heart will build a bridge of light across both time and space.
Wherever you are, our hearts still beat as one,
I hold you in my dreams each night, until your task is done.

Light up the darkness, my wondrous star,
Our hopes and dreams, my heart and yours, forever shining far.
Light up the darkness, my prince of peace;
May the stars shine all around you, may your courage never cease.

Wherever I am, I will love you day by day,
I will keep you safe, cling on to faith, along the dark, dark way.
Wherever I am, I will hold on through the night;
I will pray each day, a safe return, will look now to the light.

Greater love hath no man than this, that a man lay down his life for his friends.
John 15:13

Duration: *circa* 2½ min.

A recorded performance of *Wherever you are*, sung by The Military Wives Choir, conducted by Gareth Malone, is available on Decca, cat. no. 4764801

Order No. NOV292886;
NOV292886-10 (pack of 10) NOV292886-25 (pack of 25)

SSA and piano version NOV201146;
NOV201146-10 (pack of 10) NOV201146-25 (pack of 25)

TTBB and piano version NOV292897;
NOV292897-10 (pack of 10) NOV292897-25 (pack of 25)

Also available for SSA, piano, harp, percussion and strings NOV201135 (score)
Parts are available on hire from the publisher.

Wherever you are

The Military Wives' Prayer

PAUL MEALOR

* This line may be sung by a soloist if preferred.

28

love,_____ that___ a

- long the dark, dark way._____ Wher - ev - er I am,_____ I will

- long the dark, dark way._____ Wher - ev - er I am,_____ I will

- long the dark, dark way._____ Wher - ev - er I am,_____ I will

Ped._____ Ped._____ Ped._____

30

man_____ lay down_____ his life for_____ his

hold on through the night;_____ I will pray each day, a safe re - turn, will

hold on through the night;_____ I will pray each day, a safe re - turn, will

hold on through the night;_____ I will pray each day, a safe re - turn, will

Ped._____ Ped._____ Ped._____